The Pet Store

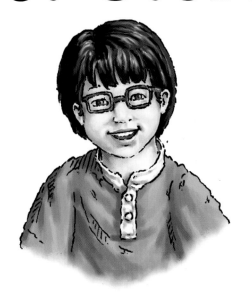

Rosemary and Hieu Nguyen
Illustrated by Tom Barrett

This is a cat.

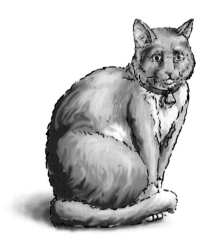

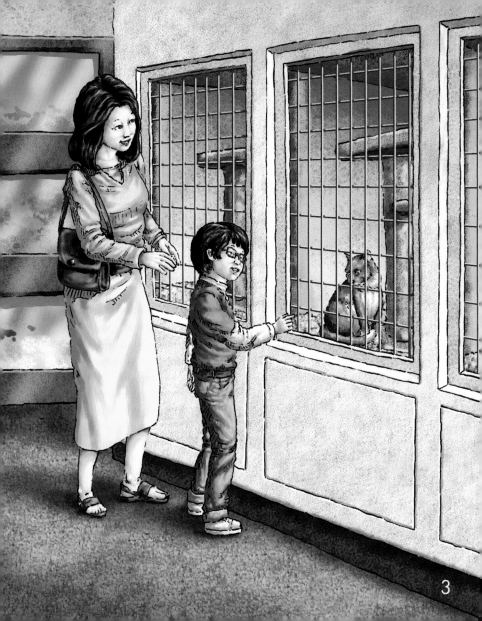

This is a dog.

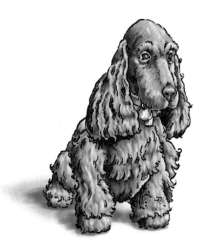

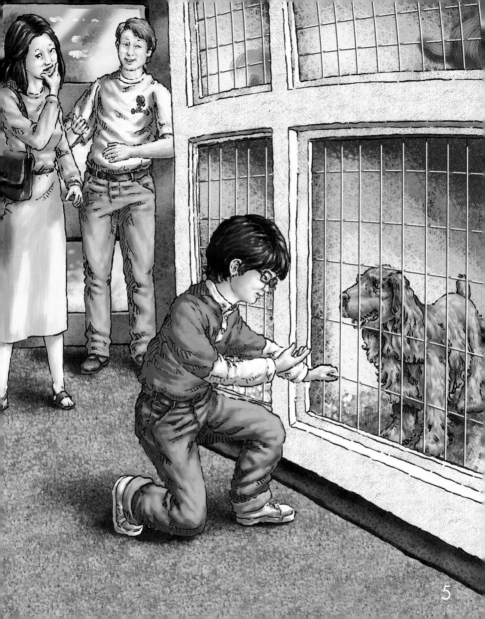

This is a bird.

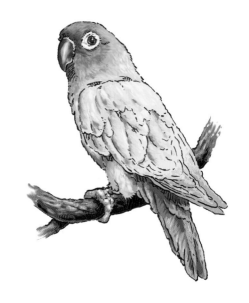

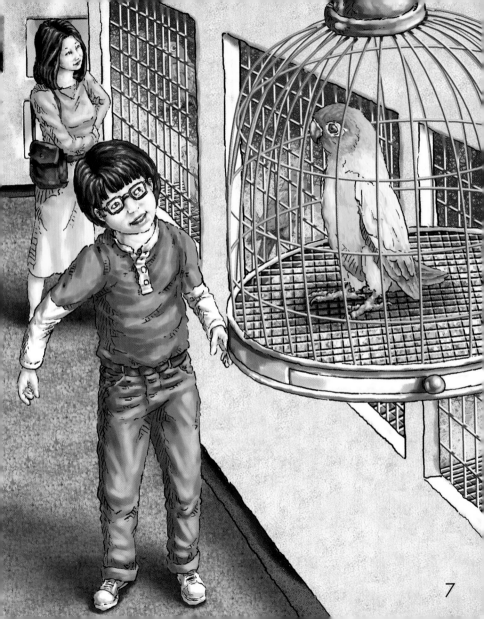

This is a mouse.

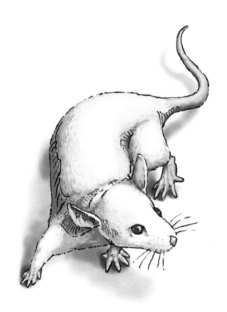

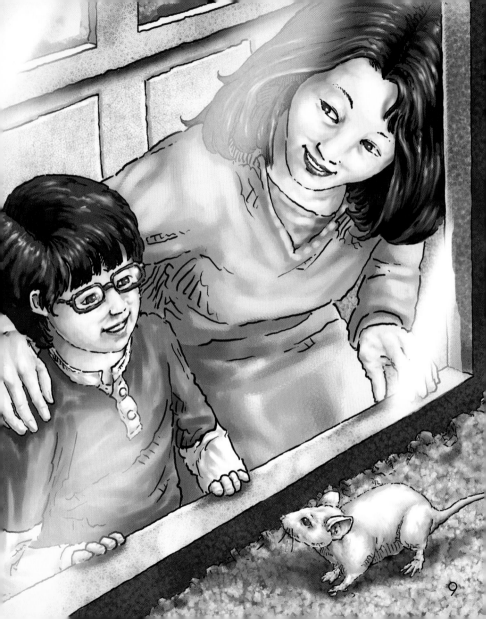

This is a lizard.

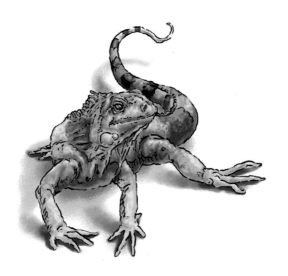

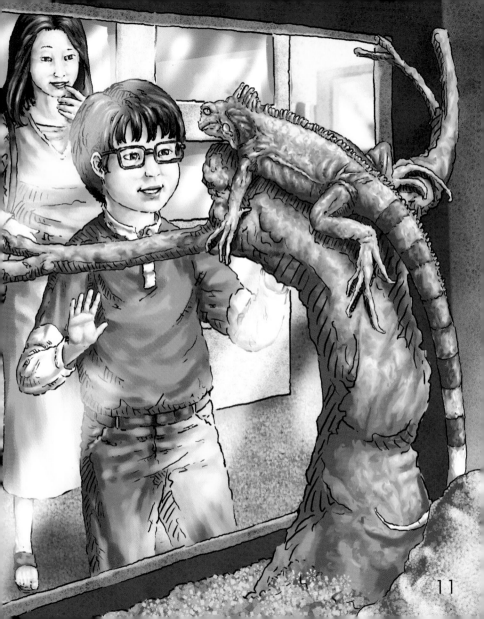

11

This is a hamster.

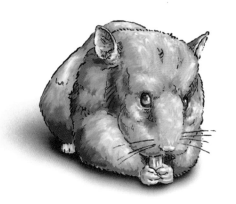

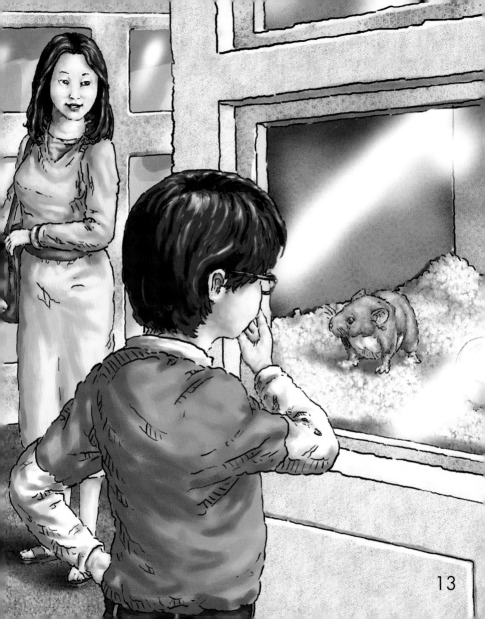

This is a fish.

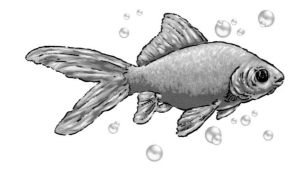

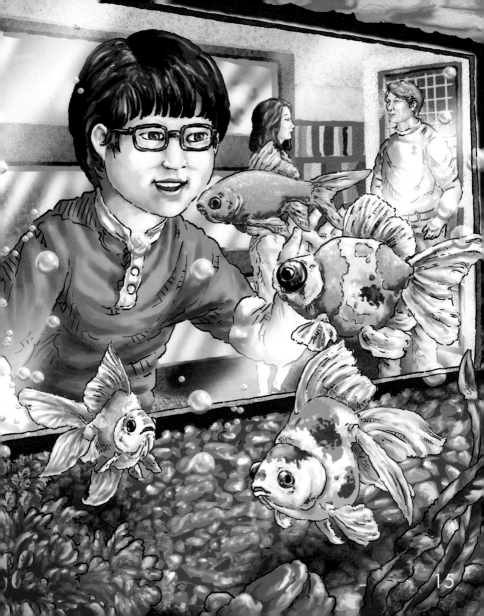

This is a pet!

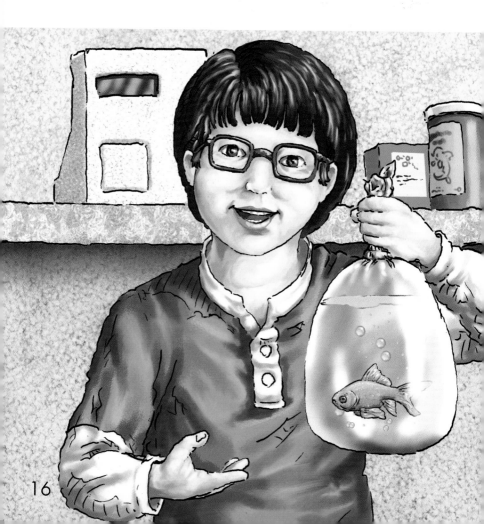